Brian Chapple

EBONY & IVORY

Five pieces in popular styles for B flat Clarinet & Piano

Contents

1 On your Marks   *page* 2

2 Out of Town   3

3 Beautifully Blue   4

4 Spanish Brandy   6

5 Gone to Lunch   7

The Associated Board of the Royal Schools of Music

EBONY & IVORY

B♭ CLARINET

BRIAN CHAPPLE

1 On your Marks

Vivace e vigoroso ma non troppo allegro ♩ = *c*.84–96, **with swing**

AB 2433

2 Out of Town

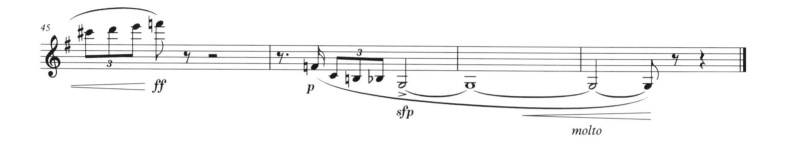

3 Beautifully Blue

4 Spanish Brandy

5 Gone to Lunch

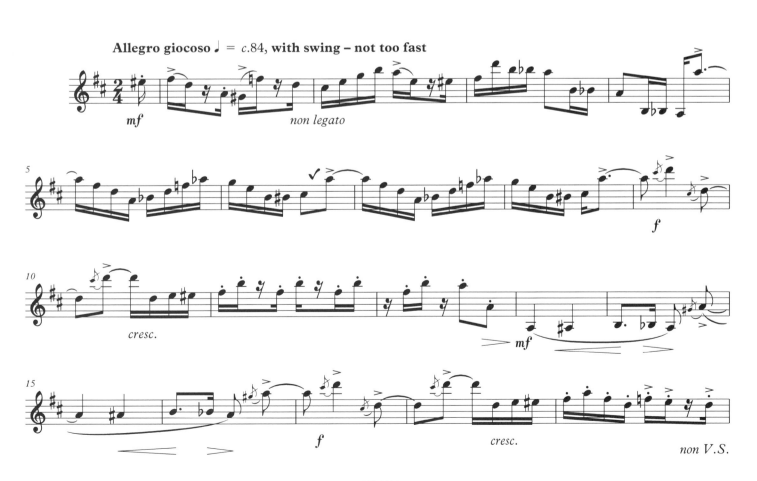

non V.S.

Printed by
Halstan & Co. Ltd., Amersham, Bucks., England

Brian Chapple

EBONY & IVORY

Five pieces in popular styles for

Clarinet & Piano

The Associated Board of the Royal Schools of Music

Contents

1 On your Marks *page* 3

2 Out of Town 5

3 Beautifully Blue 8

4 Spanish Brandy 11

5 Gone to Lunch 14

*I would like to thank David Kirby for his practical
advice in preparing these pieces for publication*

BRIAN CHAPPLE

EBONY & IVORY

BRIAN CHAPPLE

1 On your Marks

AB 2433

2 Out of Town

3 Beautifully Blue

Andante molto espress., rubato ♩ = *c.*54

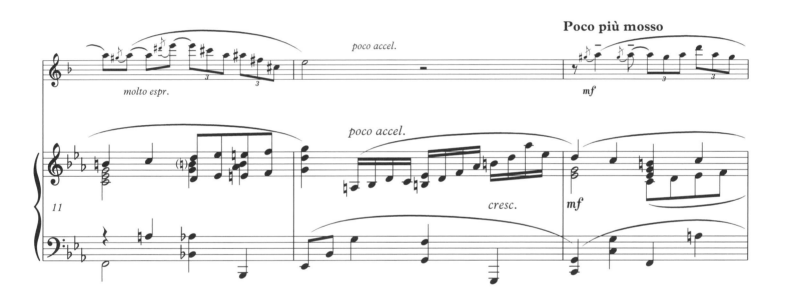

4 Spanish Brandy

Tempo di Tango ♩ = *c*.54, ♪ = *c*.108, **Molto ritmico, con fuoco**

5 Gone to Lunch

Allegro giocoso ♩ = *c*.84, **with swing – not too fast**

AB 2433

Printed by
Halstan & Co. Ltd., Amersham, Bucks., England